IMAGINE THAT

Licensed exclusively to Imagine That Publishing Ltd
Tide Mill Way, Woodbridge, Suffolk, IP12 1AP, UK
www.imaginethat.com
Copyright © 2021 Imagine That Group Ltd
All rights reserved
2 4 6 8 9 7 5 3
Manufactured in China

Written by Cece Graham
Illustrated by Róisín Hahessy

ISBN 978-1-78958-483-7

A catalogue record for this book is available from the British Library

NARWHALS LOVE NACHOS and CHEESE

Written by Cece Graham
Illustrated by Róisín Hahessy

Not many people have ever met a real-life narwhal. This is a narwhal.

'Hello!'

This is another narwhal.

'Hello!'

Boy narwhals have an extra big tooth that grows into a long spiral tusk.

It grows right through their top lip!

Some people call narwhals the 'unicorns of the sea'.

'Hello!'

Narwhals don't like this very much!

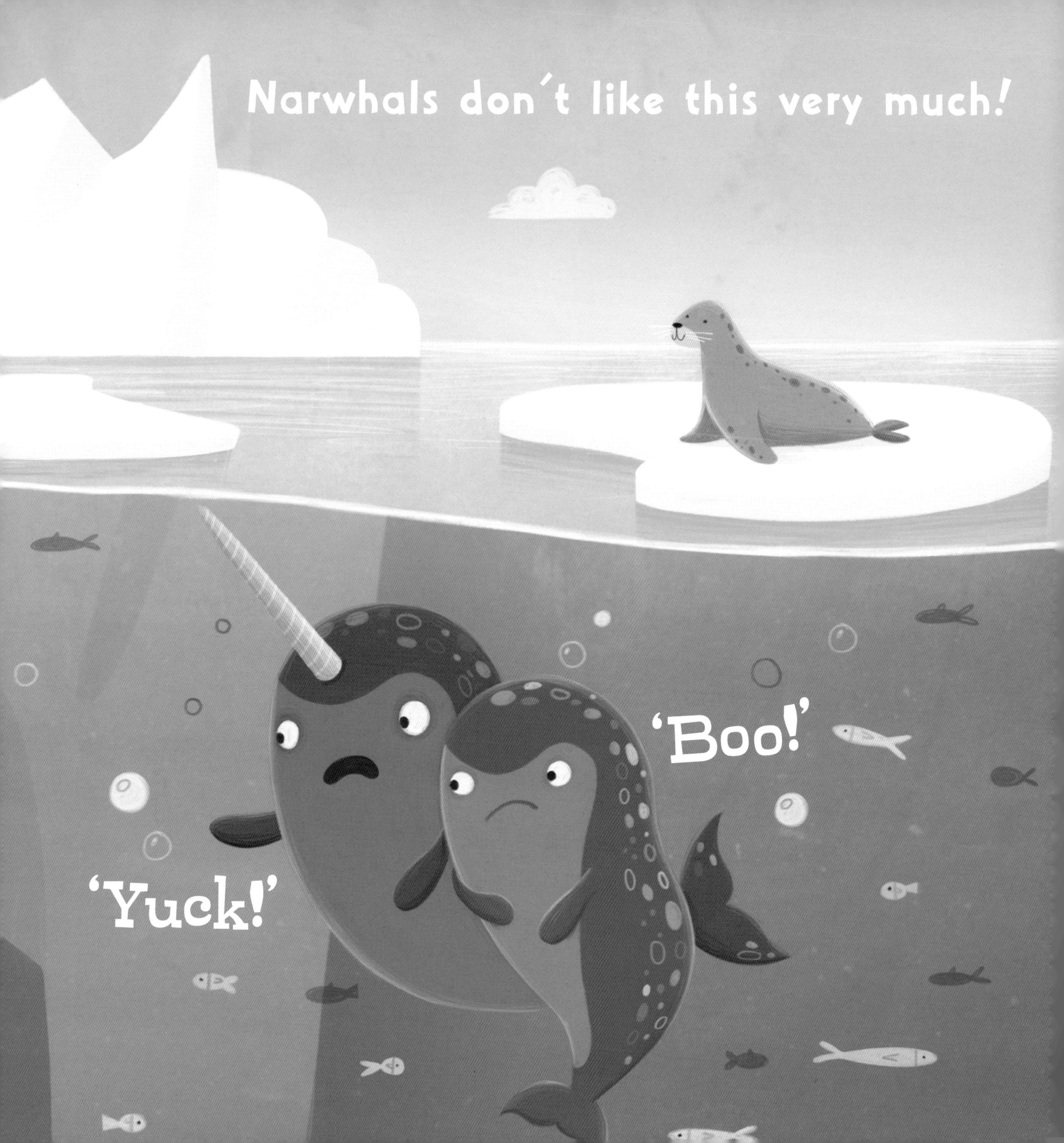

Narwhals think they are nothing
like a unicorn at all.

Splash!

'We do not have four legs,' said one narwhal.

'We have one big tail,' said the other narwhal.

Splash!

'We do not neigh,' said one narwhal.

'Whistle!'

'We are not magical,' said one narwhal.

`But we do live in a magical place,` said the other narwhal.

'We do not gallop and jump,'
said one narwhal.

`We LOVE to eat nachos and cheese,´ said the other narwhal.

`Do narwhals really love nachos and cheese?` asked a passing polar bear.

'Don´t be ridiculous!' said one narwhal.

`Narwhals love eating fish,`
said the other narwhal.

Not many people have ever met
a real-life narwhal,

but they are much funnier than unicorns!